Where do baby animals come from?

(And baby people too.)

Edited by Jane Chisholm

First published in 2012 by Usborne Publishing Ltd, 83-85 Saffron Hill, London EC1N 8RT, England.
www.usborne.com Copyright © 2012 Usborne Publishing Ltd.
 First published in America in 2012. UE. Printed in Shenzhen, Guangdong, China.

Where do baby animals come from?

(And baby people too.)

Anna Milbourne
Illustrated by Serena Riglietti

Designed by Laura Wood and Nicola Butler

Pipkin was a very small penguin who was always asking very **big** questions.

How do fish breathe underwater?

What makes winter turn to spring?

Why do stars only shine at night?

But the thing he wanted to know most of all was...

"Where do babies come from?"

He went to ask his Mama
(who was knitting something small).

"Maybe Papa can tell you,"
Pipkin's Mama said.

Pipkin went to ask his Papa
(who was keeping something warm).

"Where do babies come from?"

Papa showed Pipkin
a big, white egg.

"Well," he said, "first your Mama
lays an egg, then Papa keeps it warm..."

Just then there was a
tap,
tap,
tap...
CRACK!

"Goodness me," said Pipkin. "Babies come from eggs!"

The seal family came
to visit Pipkin's baby sister.

"Her name is Pumpkin," Pipkin proudly said.

He told his friend the seal cub,
"Babies come from eggs, you know."

But the seal cub shook his head.
"Baby seals don't come from eggs."

"Wherever do they come from,
then?" said Pipkin.

The seal cub and Pipkin talked it over
as they played in the snow.

"Seal cubs come from their Mama's tummy,"
said the seal cub. "They grow until they're ready,
then they pop out by her tail."

"If baby penguins come from eggs,
and baby seals come from their Mama's tummy,"
said Pipkin, "where do OTHER babies come from?"

The seal cub shrugged.

Pipkin said,
"I'll go and find out.
I've really got to know."

"Good luck," said the seal cub as he watched Pipkin go.

Pipkin walked to the edge of the sea,
where he met a passing whale.

"Excuse me," said Pipkin.
"Where do baby whales come from?"

"From their Mama's tummy," said the whale.
"They're born into the water and can swim right away."

"I see," said Pipkin. "Do you know where other babies come from?"

"No," said the whale.
"Perhaps you could ask some other animals.
Shall I take you to find some?"

"Yes please," said Pipkin.

The whale took Pipkin far across the sea,
until they reached another shore.

"I'll wait here for you,"
said the whale.

Pipkin went ashore and found
lots of baby turtles running to the sea.

"Excuse me," said Pipkin.
"Where do baby turtles come from?"

"From soft eggs buried in the sand," said one.
"That's where our Mama leaves us.
Then, when we hatch, we hurry to the sea.
I have to dash. Bye-bye!"

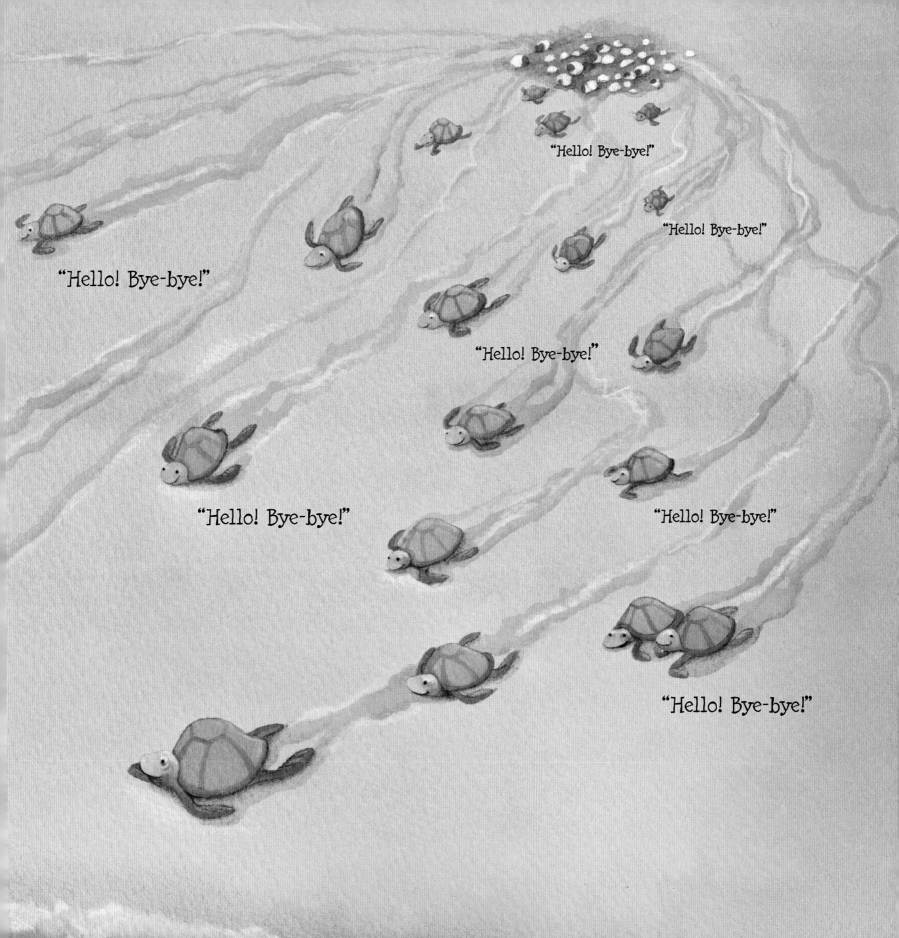

Further up the beach,
Pipkin met a little boy.

"Excuse me," he said.
"Where do baby people
come from?"

"From their Mama's tummy," said the little boy.
"My Mama's got a baby growing in hers now."

"I'm going to be a big brother soon,"
the little boy said.

"I'M a big brother..." said Pipkin.
"That reminds me - I've really got to go.
I need to tell my baby sister everything I know."

The whale took Pipkin home again
all the way across the sea.

Pipkin told his baby sister:

"There are all kinds of babies in the world,
and they're born in different ways.
Baby penguins and turtles come from eggs,
but baby seals and whales grow in their Mama's tummy.
Then, when they're ready, they pop out by her tail.
Baby people grow in their Mama's tummy too...

Some have brothers and sisters
just like me and you."

"The world is so full of interesting
things to tell you...

Night-night, my little sister," sleepy Pipkin said.

Pipkin found out more about all kinds of different babies...

Come this way to see what he discovered.